this Book
belongs to

D1416088

	☐ WEBSITE	☐ APP	☐ OTHERS
USERNAME			
PASSWORD			
NOTES			

	☐ WEBSITE	☐ APP	☐ OTHERS
USERNAME			
PASSWORD			
NOTES			

	☐ WEBSITE	☐ APP	☐ OTHERS
USERNAME			
PASSWORD			
NOTES			

	WEBSITE	APP	OTHERS
USERNAME			
PASSWORD			
NOTES			

	WEBSITE	APP	OTHERS
USERNAME			
PASSWORD			
NOTES			

	WEBSITE	APP	OTHERS
USERNAME			
PASSWORD			
NOTES			

	WEBSITE	APP	OTHERS

USERNAME

PASSWORD

NOTES

	WEBSITE	APP	OTHERS

USERNAME

PASSWORD

NOTES

	WEBSITE	APP	OTHERS

USERNAME

PASSWORD

NOTES

A

	WEBSITE	APP	OTHERS
USERNAME			
PASSWORD			
NOTES			

	WEBSITE	APP	OTHERS
USERNAME			
PASSWORD			
NOTES			

	WEBSITE	APP	OTHERS
USERNAME			
PASSWORD			
NOTES			

B

	☐ WEBSITE	☐ APP	☐ OTHERS
USERNAME			
PASSWORD			
NOTES			

	☐ WEBSITE	☐ APP	☐ OTHERS
USERNAME			
PASSWORD			
NOTES			

	☐ WEBSITE	☐ APP	☐ OTHERS
USERNAME			
PASSWORD			
NOTES			

B

	WEBSITE	APP	OTHERS
USERNAME			
PASSWORD			
NOTES			

	WEBSITE	APP	OTHERS
USERNAME			
PASSWORD			
NOTES			

	WEBSITE	APP	OTHERS
USERNAME			
PASSWORD			
NOTES			

	☐ WEBSITE	☐ APP	☐ OTHERS
USERNAME			
PASSWORD			
NOTES			

	☐ WEBSITE	☐ APP	☐ OTHERS
USERNAME			
PASSWORD			
NOTES			

	☐ WEBSITE	☐ APP	☐ OTHERS
USERNAME			
PASSWORD			
NOTES			

B

	WEBSITE	APP	OTHERS
USERNAME			
PASSWORD			
NOTES			

	WEBSITE	APP	OTHERS
USERNAME			
PASSWORD			
NOTES			

	WEBSITE	APP	OTHERS
USERNAME			
PASSWORD			
NOTES			

	WEBSITE	APP	OTHERS
USERNAME			
PASSWORD			
NOTES			

	WEBSITE	APP	OTHERS
USERNAME			
PASSWORD			
NOTES			

	WEBSITE	APP	OTHERS
USERNAME			
PASSWORD			
NOTES			

C

	WEBSITE	APP	OTHERS
USERNAME			
PASSWORD			
NOTES			

	WEBSITE	APP	OTHERS
USERNAME			
PASSWORD			
NOTES			

	WEBSITE	APP	OTHERS
USERNAME			
PASSWORD			
NOTES			

	☐ WEBSITE	☐ APP	☐ OTHERS
USERNAME			
PASSWORD			
NOTES			

	☐ WEBSITE	☐ APP	☐ OTHERS
USERNAME			
PASSWORD			
NOTES			

	☐ WEBSITE	☐ APP	☐ OTHERS
USERNAME			
PASSWORD			
NOTES			

	WEBSITE	APP	OTHERS
USERNAME			
PASSWORD			
NOTES			

	WEBSITE	APP	OTHERS
USERNAME			
PASSWORD			
NOTES			

	WEBSITE	APP	OTHERS
USERNAME			
PASSWORD			
NOTES			

WEBSITE □ APP □ OTHERS

USERNAME

PASSWORD

NOTES

WEBSITE □ APP □ OTHERS

USERNAME

PASSWORD

NOTES

WEBSITE □ APP □ OTHERS

USERNAME

PASSWORD

NOTES

D

	☐ WEBSITE	☐ APP	☐ OTHERS
USERNAME			
PASSWORD			
NOTES			

	☐ WEBSITE	☐ APP	☐ OTHERS
USERNAME			
PASSWORD			
NOTES			

	☐ WEBSITE	☐ APP	☐ OTHERS
USERNAME			
PASSWORD			
NOTES			

WEBSITE   APP   OTHERS

USERNAME

PASSWORD

NOTES

WEBSITE   APP   OTHERS

USERNAME

PASSWORD

NOTES

WEBSITE   APP   OTHERS

USERNAME

PASSWORD

NOTES

D

	☐ WEBSITE	☐ APP	☐ OTHERS
USERNAME			
PASSWORD			
NOTES			

	☐ WEBSITE	☐ APP	☐ OTHERS
USERNAME			
PASSWORD			
NOTES			

	☐ WEBSITE	☐ APP	☐ OTHERS
USERNAME			
PASSWORD			
NOTES			

	☐ WEBSITE	☐ APP	☐ OTHERS
USERNAME			
PASSWORD			
NOTES			

	☐ WEBSITE	☐ APP	☐ OTHERS
USERNAME			
PASSWORD			
NOTES			

	☐ WEBSITE	☐ APP	☐ OTHERS
USERNAME			
PASSWORD			
NOTES			

	WEBSITE	APP	OTHERS
USERNAME			
PASSWORD			
NOTES			

	WEBSITE	APP	OTHERS
USERNAME			
PASSWORD			
NOTES			

	WEBSITE	APP	OTHERS
USERNAME			
PASSWORD			
NOTES			

E

	WEBSITE	APP	OTHERS
USERNAME			
PASSWORD			
NOTES			

	WEBSITE	APP	OTHERS
USERNAME			
PASSWORD			
NOTES			

	WEBSITE	APP	OTHERS
USERNAME			
PASSWORD			
NOTES			

E

	WEBSITE	APP	OTHERS
USERNAME			
PASSWORD			
NOTES			

	WEBSITE	APP	OTHERS
USERNAME			
PASSWORD			
NOTES			

	WEBSITE	APP	OTHERS
USERNAME			
PASSWORD			
NOTES			

	WEBSITE	APP	OTHERS

USERNAME

PASSWORD

NOTES

	WEBSITE	APP	OTHERS

USERNAME

PASSWORD

NOTES

	WEBSITE	APP	OTHERS

USERNAME

PASSWORD

NOTES

F

	WEBSITE	APP	OTHERS
USERNAME			
PASSWORD			
NOTES			

	WEBSITE	APP	OTHERS
USERNAME			
PASSWORD			
NOTES			

	WEBSITE	APP	OTHERS
USERNAME			
PASSWORD			
NOTES			

	WEBSITE	APP	OTHERS
USERNAME			
PASSWORD			
NOTES			

	WEBSITE	APP	OTHERS
USERNAME			
PASSWORD			
NOTES			

	WEBSITE	APP	OTHERS
USERNAME			
PASSWORD			
NOTES			

F

	WEBSITE	APP	OTHERS
USERNAME			
PASSWORD			
NOTES			

	WEBSITE	APP	OTHERS
USERNAME			
PASSWORD			
NOTES			

	WEBSITE	APP	OTHERS
USERNAME			
PASSWORD			
NOTES			

WEBSITE ☐ APP ☐ OTHERS ☐

USERNAME

PASSWORD

NOTES

WEBSITE ☐ APP ☐ OTHERS ☐

USERNAME

PASSWORD

NOTES

WEBSITE ☐ APP ☐ OTHERS ☐

USERNAME

PASSWORD

NOTES

G

	☐ WEBSITE	☐ APP	☐ OTHERS
USERNAME			
PASSWORD			
NOTES			

	☐ WEBSITE	☐ APP	☐ OTHERS
USERNAME			
PASSWORD			
NOTES			

	☐ WEBSITE	☐ APP	☐ OTHERS
USERNAME			
PASSWORD			
NOTES			

☐ WEBSITE   ☐ APP   ☐ OTHERS

USERNAME

PASSWORD

NOTES

☐ WEBSITE   ☐ APP   ☐ OTHERS

USERNAME

PASSWORD

NOTES

☐ WEBSITE   ☐ APP   ☐ OTHERS

USERNAME

PASSWORD

NOTES

G

	WEBSITE	APP	OTHERS

USERNAME

PASSWORD

NOTES

	WEBSITE	APP	OTHERS

USERNAME

PASSWORD

NOTES

	WEBSITE	APP	OTHERS

USERNAME

PASSWORD

NOTES

H

| | WEBSITE | APP | OTHERS |

USERNAME

PASSWORD

NOTES

| | WEBSITE | APP | OTHERS |

USERNAME

PASSWORD

NOTES

| | WEBSITE | APP | OTHERS |

USERNAME

PASSWORD

NOTES

H

	WEBSITE	APP	OTHERS
USERNAME			
PASSWORD			
NOTES			

	WEBSITE	APP	OTHERS
USERNAME			
PASSWORD			
NOTES			

	WEBSITE	APP	OTHERS
USERNAME			
PASSWORD			
NOTES			

	WEBSITE	APP	OTHERS
USERNAME			
PASSWORD			
NOTES			

	WEBSITE	APP	OTHERS
USERNAME			
PASSWORD			
NOTES			

	WEBSITE	APP	OTHERS
USERNAME			
PASSWORD			
NOTES			

H

	WEBSITE	APP	OTHERS
USERNAME			
PASSWORD			
NOTES			

	WEBSITE	APP	OTHERS
USERNAME			
PASSWORD			
NOTES			

	WEBSITE	APP	OTHERS
USERNAME			
PASSWORD			
NOTES			

| | WEBSITE | APP | OTHERS |

USERNAME

PASSWORD

NOTES

| | WEBSITE | APP | OTHERS |

USERNAME

PASSWORD

NOTES

| | WEBSITE | APP | OTHERS |

USERNAME

PASSWORD

NOTES

1

	WEBSITE	APP	OTHERS
USERNAME			
PASSWORD			
NOTES			

	WEBSITE	APP	OTHERS
USERNAME			
PASSWORD			
NOTES			

	WEBSITE	APP	OTHERS
USERNAME			
PASSWORD			
NOTES			

	WEBSITE	APP	OTHERS

USERNAME

PASSWORD

NOTES

	WEBSITE	APP	OTHERS

USERNAME

PASSWORD

NOTES

	WEBSITE	APP	OTHERS

USERNAME

PASSWORD

NOTES

1

	WEBSITE	APP	OTHERS

USERNAME

PASSWORD

NOTES

	WEBSITE	APP	OTHERS

USERNAME

PASSWORD

NOTES

	WEBSITE	APP	OTHERS

USERNAME

PASSWORD

NOTES

	☐ WEBSITE	☐ APP	☐ OTHERS
USERNAME			
PASSWORD			
NOTES			

	☐ WEBSITE	☐ APP	☐ OTHERS
USERNAME			
PASSWORD			
NOTES			

	☐ WEBSITE	☐ APP	☐ OTHERS
USERNAME			
PASSWORD			
NOTES			

J

	WEBSITE	APP	OTHERS
USERNAME			
PASSWORD			
NOTES			

	WEBSITE	APP	OTHERS
USERNAME			
PASSWORD			
NOTES			

	WEBSITE	APP	OTHERS
USERNAME			
PASSWORD			
NOTES			

WEBSITE ☐　APP ☐　OTHERS ☐

USERNAME

PASSWORD

NOTES

WEBSITE ☐　APP ☐　OTHERS ☐

USERNAME

PASSWORD

NOTES

WEBSITE ☐　APP ☐　OTHERS ☐

USERNAME

PASSWORD

NOTES

J

	WEBSITE	APP	OTHERS
USERNAME			
PASSWORD			
NOTES			

	WEBSITE	APP	OTHERS
USERNAME			
PASSWORD			
NOTES			

	WEBSITE	APP	OTHERS
USERNAME			
PASSWORD			
NOTES			

	WEBSITE	APP	OTHERS
USERNAME			
PASSWORD			
NOTES			

	WEBSITE	APP	OTHERS
USERNAME			
PASSWORD			
NOTES			

	WEBSITE	APP	OTHERS
USERNAME			
PASSWORD			
NOTES			

K

WEBSITE   APP   OTHERS

USERNAME

PASSWORD

NOTES

WEBSITE   APP   OTHERS

USERNAME

PASSWORD

NOTES

WEBSITE   APP   OTHERS

USERNAME

PASSWORD

NOTES

K

| | WEBSITE | APP | OTHERS |

USERNAME

PASSWORD

NOTES

| | WEBSITE | APP | OTHERS |

USERNAME

PASSWORD

NOTES

| | WEBSITE | APP | OTHERS |

USERNAME

PASSWORD

NOTES

K

	☐ WEBSITE	☐ APP	☐ OTHERS
USERNAME			
PASSWORD			
NOTES			

	☐ WEBSITE	☐ APP	☐ OTHERS
USERNAME			
PASSWORD			
NOTES			

	☐ WEBSITE	☐ APP	☐ OTHERS
USERNAME			
PASSWORD			
NOTES			

WEBSITE   APP   OTHERS

USERNAME

PASSWORD

NOTES

WEBSITE   APP   OTHERS

USERNAME

PASSWORD

NOTES

WEBSITE   APP   OTHERS

USERNAME

PASSWORD

NOTES

L

| | WEBSITE | APP | OTHERS |

USERNAME

PASSWORD

NOTES

| | WEBSITE | APP | OTHERS |

USERNAME

PASSWORD

NOTES

| | WEBSITE | APP | OTHERS |

USERNAME

PASSWORD

NOTES

	WEBSITE	APP	OTHERS

USERNAME

PASSWORD

NOTES

	WEBSITE	APP	OTHERS

USERNAME

PASSWORD

NOTES

	WEBSITE	APP	OTHERS

USERNAME

PASSWORD

NOTES

	WEBSITE	APP	OTHERS
USERNAME			
PASSWORD			
NOTES			

	WEBSITE	APP	OTHERS
USERNAME			
PASSWORD			
NOTES			

	WEBSITE	APP	OTHERS
USERNAME			
PASSWORD			
NOTES			

| | WEBSITE | APP | OTHERS |

USERNAME

PASSWORD

NOTES

| | WEBSITE | APP | OTHERS |

USERNAME

PASSWORD

NOTES

| | WEBSITE | APP | OTHERS |

USERNAME

PASSWORD

NOTES

M

	☐ WEBSITE	☐ APP	☐ OTHERS

USERNAME

PASSWORD

NOTES

	☐ WEBSITE	☐ APP	☐ OTHERS

USERNAME

PASSWORD

NOTES

	☐ WEBSITE	☐ APP	☐ OTHERS

USERNAME

PASSWORD

NOTES

	WEBSITE	APP	OTHERS
USERNAME			
PASSWORD			
NOTES			

	WEBSITE	APP	OTHERS
USERNAME			
PASSWORD			
NOTES			

	WEBSITE	APP	OTHERS
USERNAME			
PASSWORD			
NOTES			

	WEBSITE	APP	OTHERS
USERNAME			
PASSWORD			
NOTES			

	WEBSITE	APP	OTHERS
USERNAME			
PASSWORD			
NOTES			

	WEBSITE	APP	OTHERS
USERNAME			
PASSWORD			
NOTES			

	WEBSITE	APP	OTHERS

USERNAME

PASSWORD

NOTES

	WEBSITE	APP	OTHERS

USERNAME

PASSWORD

NOTES

	WEBSITE	APP	OTHERS

USERNAME

PASSWORD

NOTES

	WEBSITE	APP	OTHERS
USERNAME			
PASSWORD			
NOTES			

	WEBSITE	APP	OTHERS
USERNAME			
PASSWORD			
NOTES			

	WEBSITE	APP	OTHERS
USERNAME			
PASSWORD			
NOTES			

| | WEBSITE | APP | OTHERS |

USERNAME

PASSWORD

NOTES

| | WEBSITE | APP | OTHERS |

USERNAME

PASSWORD

NOTES

| | WEBSITE | APP | OTHERS |

USERNAME

PASSWORD

NOTES

| | WEBSITE | APP | OTHERS |

USERNAME

PASSWORD

NOTES

| | WEBSITE | APP | OTHERS |

USERNAME

PASSWORD

NOTES

| | WEBSITE | APP | OTHERS |

USERNAME

PASSWORD

NOTES

	WEBSITE	APP	OTHERS
USERNAME			
PASSWORD			
NOTES			

	WEBSITE	APP	OTHERS
USERNAME			
PASSWORD			
NOTES			

	WEBSITE	APP	OTHERS
USERNAME			
PASSWORD			
NOTES			

O

	WEBSITE	APP	OTHERS
USERNAME			
PASSWORD			
NOTES			

	WEBSITE	APP	OTHERS
USERNAME			
PASSWORD			
NOTES			

	WEBSITE	APP	OTHERS
USERNAME			
PASSWORD			
NOTES			

USERNAME

PASSWORD

NOTES

WEBSITE ☐ APP ☐ OTHERS ☐

USERNAME

PASSWORD

NOTES

WEBSITE ☐ APP ☐ OTHERS ☐

USERNAME

PASSWORD

NOTES

WEBSITE ☐ APP ☐ OTHERS ☐

O

	WEBSITE	APP	OTHERS
USERNAME			
PASSWORD			
NOTES			

	WEBSITE	APP	OTHERS
USERNAME			
PASSWORD			
NOTES			

	WEBSITE	APP	OTHERS
USERNAME			
PASSWORD			
NOTES			

WEBSITE   APP   OTHERS

USERNAME

PASSWORD

NOTES

WEBSITE   APP   OTHERS

USERNAME

PASSWORD

NOTES

WEBSITE   APP   OTHERS

USERNAME

PASSWORD

NOTES

	WEBSITE	APP	OTHERS
USERNAME			
PASSWORD			
NOTES			

	WEBSITE	APP	OTHERS
USERNAME			
PASSWORD			
NOTES			

	WEBSITE	APP	OTHERS
USERNAME			
PASSWORD			
NOTES			

	WEBSITE	APP	OTHERS

USERNAME

PASSWORD

NOTES

	WEBSITE	APP	OTHERS

USERNAME

PASSWORD

NOTES

	WEBSITE	APP	OTHERS

USERNAME

PASSWORD

NOTES

P

	WEBSITE	APP	OTHERS
USERNAME			
PASSWORD			
NOTES			

	WEBSITE	APP	OTHERS
USERNAME			
PASSWORD			
NOTES			

	WEBSITE	APP	OTHERS
USERNAME			
PASSWORD			
NOTES			

WEBSITE ☐   APP ☐   OTHERS ☐

USERNAME

PASSWORD

NOTES

WEBSITE ☐   APP ☐   OTHERS ☐

USERNAME

PASSWORD

NOTES

WEBSITE ☐   APP ☐   OTHERS ☐

USERNAME

PASSWORD

NOTES

	WEBSITE	APP	OTHERS

USERNAME

PASSWORD

NOTES

	WEBSITE	APP	OTHERS

USERNAME

PASSWORD

NOTES

	WEBSITE	APP	OTHERS

USERNAME

PASSWORD

NOTES

	WEBSITE	APP	OTHERS

USERNAME

PASSWORD

NOTES

	WEBSITE	APP	OTHERS

USERNAME

PASSWORD

NOTES

	WEBSITE	APP	OTHERS

USERNAME

PASSWORD

NOTES

	WEBSITE	APP	OTHERS
USERNAME			
PASSWORD			
NOTES			

	WEBSITE	APP	OTHERS
USERNAME			
PASSWORD			
NOTES			

	WEBSITE	APP	OTHERS
USERNAME			
PASSWORD			
NOTES			

	WEBSITE	APP	OTHERS

USERNAME

PASSWORD

NOTES

	WEBSITE	APP	OTHERS

USERNAME

PASSWORD

NOTES

	WEBSITE	APP	OTHERS

USERNAME

PASSWORD

NOTES

	WEBSITE	APP	OTHERS
USERNAME			
PASSWORD			
NOTES			

	WEBSITE	APP	OTHERS
USERNAME			
PASSWORD			
NOTES			

	WEBSITE	APP	OTHERS
USERNAME			
PASSWORD			
NOTES			

	WEBSITE	APP	OTHERS
USERNAME			
PASSWORD			
NOTES			

	WEBSITE	APP	OTHERS
USERNAME			
PASSWORD			
NOTES			

	WEBSITE	APP	OTHERS
USERNAME			
PASSWORD			
NOTES			

WEBSITE ☐   APP ☐   OTHERS ☐

USERNAME

PASSWORD

NOTES

WEBSITE ☐   APP ☐   OTHERS ☐

USERNAME

PASSWORD

NOTES

WEBSITE ☐   APP ☐   OTHERS ☐

USERNAME

PASSWORD

NOTES

	WEBSITE	APP	OTHERS

USERNAME

PASSWORD

NOTES

	WEBSITE	APP	OTHERS

USERNAME

PASSWORD

NOTES

	WEBSITE	APP	OTHERS

USERNAME

PASSWORD

NOTES

	WEBSITE	APP	OTHERS
USERNAME			
PASSWORD			
NOTES			

	WEBSITE	APP	OTHERS
USERNAME			
PASSWORD			
NOTES			

	WEBSITE	APP	OTHERS
USERNAME			
PASSWORD			
NOTES			

WEBSITE   APP   OTHERS

USERNAME

PASSWORD

NOTES

WEBSITE   APP   OTHERS

USERNAME

PASSWORD

NOTES

WEBSITE   APP   OTHERS

USERNAME

PASSWORD

NOTES

S

WEBSITE   APP   OTHERS

USERNAME

PASSWORD

NOTES

WEBSITE   APP   OTHERS

USERNAME

PASSWORD

NOTES

WEBSITE   APP   OTHERS

USERNAME

PASSWORD

NOTES

WEBSITE APP OTHERS

USERNAME

PASSWORD

NOTES

WEBSITE APP OTHERS

USERNAME

PASSWORD

NOTES

WEBSITE APP OTHERS

USERNAME

PASSWORD

NOTES

	WEBSITE	APP	OTHERS
USERNAME			
PASSWORD			
NOTES			

	WEBSITE	APP	OTHERS
USERNAME			
PASSWORD			
NOTES			

	WEBSITE	APP	OTHERS
USERNAME			
PASSWORD			
NOTES			

	WEBSITE	APP	OTHERS

USERNAME

PASSWORD

NOTES

	WEBSITE	APP	OTHERS

USERNAME

PASSWORD

NOTES

	WEBSITE	APP	OTHERS

USERNAME

PASSWORD

NOTES

	WEBSITE	APP	OTHERS
USERNAME			
PASSWORD			
NOTES			

	WEBSITE	APP	OTHERS
USERNAME			
PASSWORD			
NOTES			

	WEBSITE	APP	OTHERS
USERNAME			
PASSWORD			
NOTES			

U

| | ☐ WEBSITE | ☐ APP | ☐ OTHERS |

USERNAME

PASSWORD

NOTES

| | ☐ WEBSITE | ☐ APP | ☐ OTHERS |

USERNAME

PASSWORD

NOTES

| | ☐ WEBSITE | ☐ APP | ☐ OTHERS |

USERNAME

PASSWORD

NOTES

	WEBSITE	APP	OTHERS
USERNAME			
PASSWORD			
NOTES			

	WEBSITE	APP	OTHERS
USERNAME			
PASSWORD			
NOTES			

	WEBSITE	APP	OTHERS
USERNAME			
PASSWORD			
NOTES			

	WEBSITE	APP	OTHERS
USERNAME			
PASSWORD			
NOTES			

	WEBSITE	APP	OTHERS
USERNAME			
PASSWORD			
NOTES			

	WEBSITE	APP	OTHERS
USERNAME			
PASSWORD			
NOTES			

	WEBSITE	APP	OTHERS
USERNAME			
PASSWORD			
NOTES			

	WEBSITE	APP	OTHERS
USERNAME			
PASSWORD			
NOTES			

	WEBSITE	APP	OTHERS
USERNAME			
PASSWORD			
NOTES			

	WEBSITE	APP	OTHERS
USERNAME			
PASSWORD			
NOTES			

	WEBSITE	APP	OTHERS
USERNAME			
PASSWORD			
NOTES			

	WEBSITE	APP	OTHERS
USERNAME			
PASSWORD			
NOTES			

WEBSITE ☐ APP ☐ OTHERS ☐

USERNAME

PASSWORD

NOTES

WEBSITE ☐ APP ☐ OTHERS ☐

USERNAME

PASSWORD

NOTES

WEBSITE ☐ APP ☐ OTHERS ☐

USERNAME

PASSWORD

NOTES

WEBSITE　　APP　　OTHERS

USERNAME

PASSWORD

NOTES

WEBSITE　　APP　　OTHERS

USERNAME

PASSWORD

NOTES

WEBSITE　　APP　　OTHERS

USERNAME

PASSWORD

NOTES

WEBSITE ☐   APP ☐   OTHERS ☐

USERNAME

PASSWORD

NOTES

WEBSITE ☐   APP ☐   OTHERS ☐

USERNAME

PASSWORD

NOTES

WEBSITE ☐   APP ☐   OTHERS ☐

USERNAME

PASSWORD

NOTES

| | WEBSITE | APP | OTHERS |

USERNAME

PASSWORD

NOTES

| | WEBSITE | APP | OTHERS |

USERNAME

PASSWORD

NOTES

| | WEBSITE | APP | OTHERS |

USERNAME

PASSWORD

NOTES

	WEBSITE	APP	OTHERS
USERNAME			
PASSWORD			
NOTES			

	WEBSITE	APP	OTHERS
USERNAME			
PASSWORD			
NOTES			

	WEBSITE	APP	OTHERS
USERNAME			
PASSWORD			
NOTES			

	WEBSITE	APP	OTHERS
USERNAME			
PASSWORD			
NOTES			

	WEBSITE	APP	OTHERS
USERNAME			
PASSWORD			
NOTES			

	WEBSITE	APP	OTHERS
USERNAME			
PASSWORD			
NOTES			

	WEBSITE	APP	OTHERS

USERNAME

PASSWORD

NOTES

	WEBSITE	APP	OTHERS

USERNAME

PASSWORD

NOTES

	WEBSITE	APP	OTHERS

USERNAME

PASSWORD

NOTES

	WEBSITE	APP	OTHERS
USERNAME			
PASSWORD			
NOTES			

	WEBSITE	APP	OTHERS
USERNAME			
PASSWORD			
NOTES			

	WEBSITE	APP	OTHERS
USERNAME			
PASSWORD			
NOTES			

	WEBSITE	APP	OTHERS

USERNAME

PASSWORD

NOTES

	WEBSITE	APP	OTHERS

USERNAME

PASSWORD

NOTES

	WEBSITE	APP	OTHERS

USERNAME

PASSWORD

NOTES

WEBSITE □   APP □   OTHERS □

USERNAME

PASSWORD

NOTES

WEBSITE □   APP □   OTHERS □

USERNAME

PASSWORD

NOTES

WEBSITE □   APP □   OTHERS □

USERNAME

PASSWORD

NOTES

| | ☐ WEBSITE | ☐ APP | ☐ OTHERS |

USERNAME

PASSWORD

NOTES

| | ☐ WEBSITE | ☐ APP | ☐ OTHERS |

USERNAME

PASSWORD

NOTES

| | ☐ WEBSITE | ☐ APP | ☐ OTHERS |

USERNAME

PASSWORD

NOTES

	☐ WEBSITE	☐ APP	☐ OTHERS

USERNAME

PASSWORD

NOTES

	☐ WEBSITE	☐ APP	☐ OTHERS

USERNAME

PASSWORD

NOTES

	☐ WEBSITE	☐ APP	☐ OTHERS

USERNAME

PASSWORD

NOTES

	☐ WEBSITE	☐ APP	☐ OTHERS
USERNAME			
PASSWORD			
NOTES			

	☐ WEBSITE	☐ APP	☐ OTHERS
USERNAME			
PASSWORD			
NOTES			

	☐ WEBSITE	☐ APP	☐ OTHERS
USERNAME			
PASSWORD			
NOTES			

	WEBSITE	APP	OTHERS

USERNAME

PASSWORD

NOTES

	WEBSITE	APP	OTHERS

USERNAME

PASSWORD

NOTES

	WEBSITE	APP	OTHERS

USERNAME

PASSWORD

NOTES

Y

	WEBSITE	APP	OTHERS
USERNAME			
PASSWORD			
NOTES			

	WEBSITE	APP	OTHERS
USERNAME			
PASSWORD			
NOTES			

	WEBSITE	APP	OTHERS
USERNAME			
PASSWORD			
NOTES			

Z

	WEBSITE	APP	OTHERS
USERNAME			
PASSWORD			
NOTES			

	WEBSITE	APP	OTHERS
USERNAME			
PASSWORD			
NOTES			

	WEBSITE	APP	OTHERS
USERNAME			
PASSWORD			
NOTES			

Z

	WEBSITE	APP	OTHERS

USERNAME

PASSWORD

NOTES

	WEBSITE	APP	OTHERS

USERNAME

PASSWORD

NOTES

	WEBSITE	APP	OTHERS

USERNAME

PASSWORD

NOTES

Z

| | WEBSITE | APP | OTHERS |

USERNAME

PASSWORD

NOTES

| | WEBSITE | APP | OTHERS |

USERNAME

PASSWORD

NOTES

| | WEBSITE | APP | OTHERS |

USERNAME

PASSWORD

NOTES

Z

	WEBSITE	APP	OTHERS
USERNAME			
PASSWORD			
NOTES			

	WEBSITE	APP	OTHERS
USERNAME			
PASSWORD			
NOTES			

	WEBSITE	APP	OTHERS
USERNAME			
PASSWORD			
NOTES			

SUBSCRIPTION TRACKER

WEBSITE ☐   APP ☐   OTHERS ☐

USERNAME

PASSWORD

CREDIT CARD

PHONE

START DATE   END DATE

MONTHLY FEE   ANNUAL FEE

NOTES

WEBSITE ☐   APP ☐   OTHERS ☐

USERNAME

PASSWORD

CREDIT CARD

PHONE

START DATE   END DATE

MONTHLY FEE   ANNUAL FEE

NOTES

SUBSCRIPTION TRACKER

☐ WEBSITE   ☐ APP   ☐ OTHERS

USERNAME

PASSWORD

CREDIT CARD

PHONE

START DATE   END DATE

MONTHLY FEE   ANNUAL FEE

NOTES

☐ WEBSITE   ☐ APP   ☐ OTHERS

USERNAME

PASSWORD

CREDIT CARD

PHONE

START DATE   END DATE

MONTHLY FEE   ANNUAL FEE

NOTES

SUBSCRIPTION TRACKER

	WEBSITE	APP	OTHERS
USERNAME			
PASSWORD			
CREDIT CARD			
PHONE			
START DATE		END DATE	
MONTHLY FEE		ANNUAL FEE	
NOTES			

	WEBSITE	APP	OTHERS
USERNAME			
PASSWORD			
CREDIT CARD			
PHONE			
START DATE		END DATE	
MONTHLY FEE		ANNUAL FEE	
NOTES			

SUBSCRIPTION TRACKER

☐ WEBSITE   ☐ APP   ☐ OTHERS

USERNAME

PASSWORD

CREDIT CARD

PHONE

START DATE   END DATE

MONTHLY FEE   ANNUAL FEE

NOTES

☐ WEBSITE   ☐ APP   ☐ OTHERS

USERNAME

PASSWORD

CREDIT CARD

PHONE

START DATE   END DATE

MONTHLY FEE   ANNUAL FEE

NOTES

SUBSCRIPTION TRACKER

	WEBSITE	APP	OTHERS

USERNAME

PASSWORD

CREDIT CARD

PHONE

START DATE   END DATE

MONTHLY FEE   ANNUAL FEE

NOTES

	WEBSITE	APP	OTHERS

USERNAME

PASSWORD

CREDIT CARD

PHONE

START DATE   END DATE

MONTHLY FEE   ANNUAL FEE

NOTES

SUBSCRIPTION TRACKER

☐ WEBSITE ☐ APP ☐ OTHERS

USERNAME

PASSWORD

CREDIT CARD

PHONE

START DATE   END DATE

MONTHLY FEE   ANNUAL FEE

NOTES

☐ WEBSITE ☐ APP ☐ OTHERS

USERNAME

PASSWORD

CREDIT CARD

PHONE

START DATE   END DATE

MONTHLY FEE   ANNUAL FEE

NOTES

SUBSCRIPTION TRACKER

	WEBSITE	APP	OTHERS

USERNAME

PASSWORD

CREDIT CARD

PHONE

START DATE   END DATE

MONTHLY FEE   ANNUAL FEE

NOTES

	WEBSITE	APP	OTHERS

USERNAME

PASSWORD

CREDIT CARD

PHONE

START DATE   END DATE

MONTHLY FEE   ANNUAL FEE

NOTES

SUBSCRIPTION TRACKER

☐ WEBSITE   ☐ APP   ☐ OTHERS

USERNAME

PASSWORD

CREDIT CARD

PHONE

START DATE   END DATE

MONTHLY FEE   ANNUAL FEE

NOTES

☐ WEBSITE   ☐ APP   ☐ OTHERS

USERNAME

PASSWORD

CREDIT CARD

PHONE

START DATE   END DATE

MONTHLY FEE   ANNUAL FEE

NOTES

NOTES

NOTES

NOTES

NOTES

NOTES

NOTES

NOTES

NOTES

Made in United States
North Haven, CT
09 February 2022

15919577R00070